Tilly
A RIVER OTTER

by Bonnie Highsmith Taylor

Perfection Learning®

Dedication

For Margaret Gillenwater

About the Author

Bonnie Highsmith Taylor is a native Oregonian. She loves camping in the Oregon mountains and watching birds and other wildlife. Writing is Ms. Taylor's first love. But she also enjoys going to plays and concerts, collecting antique dolls, and listening to good music.

Ms. Taylor is the author of several Animal Adventures books, including *Kip: A Sea Otter* and *Roscoe: A North American Moose*.

Cover Photo: Michael H. Francis

Image Credits: Michael H. Francis pp. 6, 10, 13, 19, 27, 31, 33, 40, 46–47

EyeWire p. 8; ArtToday (some images copyright www.arttoday.com); Corel Professional Photos pp. 5, 16, 17, 21, 22, 29, 42–43, 44–45, 50–51, 52; Corel.com p. 38

CONTENTS

It was the middle of April. Snow still covered the ground. But the den in the riverbank was warm and snug.

Many river otters make their homes in hollow logs or tree roots. Others choose empty muskrat houses or woodchuck burrows. But all their homes must be near water.

Some otters make their homes in swampy areas. They twist grasses and reeds together at the top. The nests look like small teepees.

In the den, a two-year-old female otter had just given birth for the first time. Her nest was made of sticks and grasses. The mother had three babies.

Tilly was the only female in the litter. Like her brothers, her eyes were tightly closed. She was covered with soft fur. But this fur was not waterproof.

The babies were about seven inches long. They weighed between three and four ounces.

The largest otters are found in Brazil. They are about eight feet long.

American otters are about 45 to 50 inches long. Their average weight is 15 to 20 pounds. Females are smaller than males.

The mother otter washed her babies. They squirmed and made soft peeping sounds. They sounded just like baby birds.

The mother finished cleaning them. Then she curled her body around her babies. Inside the warm circle, the little ones slept.

Outside the den, the river splashed over rocks and logs. Overhead, an osprey

soared around and around. Suddenly, it swooped down over the river. It grabbed a trout in its claws and carried it off.

The father otter roamed up and down the riverbank. Twice he tried to enter the den. But his mate snarled at him. She would not let him around the babies until they were several weeks old.

After a while, the father otter wandered off by himself. But he would not go too far away.

The babies woke up. Tilly worked her tiny feet against her mother's belly as she nursed. This made the milk flow faster.

Otters have very rich milk. The rich milk makes the babies grow quickly.

After the babies had filled their stomachs, the mother cleaned them again. She licked the urine and feces from their bodies. This was to keep the den clean.

The mother was very hungry. She left the den and slid into the river. It was not long before she was able to catch a fish.

It was easy to catch. The fish had stayed near its eggs.

The otter took the fish to the flat rock. She tore off the scales before she ate it. She chewed the head before eating the rest of the fish. Then she caught a sunfish and a salamander.

Many fishermen feel that river otters eat too many game fish. It is true that otters will eat trout and salmon when they can. But salmon and trout move fast in the water. They are harder to catch than other fish.

More often, otters eat slower-moving fish. They eat catfish, carp, suckers, and sunfish. These fish feed on trout and salmon eggs.

Otters eat crayfish, turtles, salamanders, frogs, and water snakes. They also enjoy water insects, snails, and worms.

Ground-nesting birds and their eggs, mice, and other smaller mammals are part of an otter's diet. Sometimes otters even catch ducks. They swim under the ducks and grab them by their legs.

Otters eat some vegetation—like grass, pondweeds, algae, and berries.

In all, otters eat about three pounds of food a day.

After the mother otter finished her meal, she cleaned herself. She rolled over and over in the water. Then she climbed onto the bank and shook herself hard.

The mother was full and clean now. She crawled back into the den. She curled herself around her sleeping babies. Then she slept too.

CHAPTER 2

Tilly was ten days old. She and her brothers were growing fast. They weighed nearly a pound each. Most of their time was spent sleeping and nursing.

The mother otter left the nest often. She had to eat and exercise. She grew cramped inside the den.

She never went far from the den. The snow had melted, and the air was a little warmer. So sometimes she basked in the sun.

The mother otter slipped into the water. She began to search for food.

Otters have sharp eyesight and a keen sense of touch. It's believed that otters see underwater better than above. Their eyes have many light-sensitive rods. These give the animals sharp vision in water, even if it's muddy. A strong sense of touch helps them find food even when it's hidden.

The female felt under some rocks with her paws. She found a crayfish.

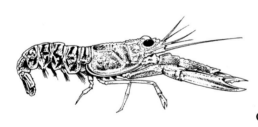

She climbed onto a log that lay in the water. She ate all of the crayfish but the claws.

Then back into the water she went. With her long whiskers, she could feel a vibration in the water. Something was moving close to her.

It was a muskrat. She made a dive for it. But this time she was not fast enough.

For a while, she swam on the surface of the water. She looked all around as she swam.

Otters can swim about six miles an hour on the surface. Underwater, they swim about three to four miles an hour.

River otters can stay underwater for about four minutes. Then they have to come up for air. They can swim on their backs as well as on their stomachs.

Another otter swam past the female. At once, she swam toward it. She was not trying to run it off. She wanted to play.

Otters love to play. It doesn't matter how old they are.

For a long time, the female otter frisked about with the other otter. Over and over in the water they flipped. They chased each other over rocks and under logs.

Finally, the otters came out of the water. On the bank, they shook themselves dry. Then they began to groom each other. They fluffed each other's fur.

After the stranger left, the mother went back to her babies.

River otters are part of the weasel family. Like all members of the weasel family, otters have scent glands. But they have very little odor.

River otter

Their cousin, the sea otter, does not have these glands. Sea otters live only in the Pacific Ocean from Alaska to California.

Sea otter

River otters can be found on every continent but Australia and Antarctica. They live in most parts of the United States. For many years, otters were trapped and hunted heavily. Few are left in some states.

But now, the river otters are being returned to some places where they were nearly wiped out. They're back in Oklahoma and Colorado.

In 1982, animal biologists began moving otters back to Missouri. Now over 2,000 otters are living in the waterways there.

This animal that was once nearly destroyed by humans is now being saved by humans.

But there are still problems with otters' habitats. Wetlands have been filled in. Waterways have been polluted by toxins used in agriculture and industry.

CHAPTER

Tilly and her brothers were about five weeks old. Their eyes were open. They had shed their baby fur. Their waterproof coats were growing thick.

River otters have very thick, plush fur. On their backs are waterproof guard hairs. These are about an inch long. The woolly underfur is about three-quarters of an inch long. The guard hairs and the underfur on otters' bellies are shorter than on their backs. The underfur keeps water from reaching the skin.

Otters also have a layer of fat. The fat keeps the otters warm in very cold water and in cold weather.

Sea otters have much thicker hair. But they don't have fat layers. It is believed that sea otters have over a billion hairs.

The babies spent a lot of time wrestling in the den. Tilly could hold her own with her brothers.

The mother otter played with her babies a lot. And she kept them clean and well-groomed. The babies were growing fast on their mother's rich milk.

Songbirds were returning to the area. They had spent the winter in the South. They were building nests in trees along the riverbank.

Fawns were being born. They lay in the tall grass. Their mothers had hidden them there. Their spots kept them from being seen easily by coyotes and mountain lions.

In the meadows in deep dens, baby foxes were stirring. They were ready to come out into the big world. Other dens were full of baby coyotes, bobcats, and woodchucks.

One day, a mother black bear and her small cub came to the river to drink.

The mother otter sat
in the opening of
her den. She watched
them. She was curious.
What were these big,
strange animals?

She came out of the den
and stood on the riverbank.
She stood on her hind
legs and stretched as
tall as she could. Her eyes grew big. She made a
chuckling sound.

The bear cub saw the otter. It stared. Then it
started toward her. The mother otter stretched
herself taller and taller.

The cub had only taken a couple of steps
when its mother grunted. The cub knew that
meant "Get back here." It turned and went back
to its mother.

The otter was still standing on her hind legs. She watched as the mother bear and her cub walked away.

The otter walked slowly to where the bears had stood on the riverbank. She sniffed the ground. What a different smell.

Then she began turning over rocks. She picked snails from off the rocks and ate them.

Bored, she crawled back into the den. Maybe her babies were awake. She would play with them.

One day, Tilly crept to the opening of the den. Her brothers were sleeping.

Tilly came nearly all the way out. But she stopped suddenly. She could smell her mother. But there was another smell.

Tilly peeked out. There was Mama. But another otter was there too. It was bigger than Mama. Who was that? Would it hurt her?

She started back into the den. But just then, her mother made a chattering noise in her throat. She was calling Tilly. But Tilly didn't want to leave the safety of the den. She was afraid of the other otter. It might hurt her.

The mother otter called Tilly again. Very slowly and fearfully, Tilly crept out. Her mother nudged Tilly with her nose. She blew her breath on Tilly, ruffling her hair.

The big otter came closer. Tilly shook while he sniffed her all over.

Tilly could smell him very well now. But it wasn't a bad smell. It was a smell almost like her mother's.

Tilly's brothers woke up. They crawled out of the den. They, too, were fearful. The mother made a noise that meant "Come."

Slowly, the brothers came to their mother. The big otter sniffed them too. Then he grunted softly. He was saying, "Don't be afraid. I'm your father."

Cases are known of
male otters taking care
of their babies
when the
mother was
killed. But
those babies
were already
weaned. They no longer
needed their mother's milk.

Tilly discovered that her father was as
nice as her mother. He played with her and
her brothers. He groomed them. There was
only one thing wrong. Father didn't have a
place for them to get sweet, warm milk.

CHAPTER

Tilly and her brothers spent a lot of time out of the den now. They had two parents to watch out for them.

One day, Tilly's father saved her life. It was stormy. The wind was blowing hard. Big raindrops fell. A light fog drifted over the river.

The mother otter was inside the den nursing her babies. Tilly was full. Her mother and brothers fell asleep. But Tilly was not sleepy. She wanted to play. She crawled out of the nest and went outside.

The father otter had just come out of the water. He had a large bass in his mouth. He put it on the ground and began to chew on it. Tilly edged a little closer. The smell of the fish was not new to her. Her mother often had the same smell on her.

Tilly sniffed the bass while her father chewed on it. She licked a little drop of blood on the fish's tail. She twitched her nose. She licked some more. It was good.

She was ready to take a bite. Suddenly, a dark figure zoomed down from above. It was an eagle. The father otter let out a loud, piercing scream. At the same time, he discharged a milky fluid.

The fluid did not hit the eagle. Even if it had, it would not have had the same effect as a skunk's fluid. It does smell bad. But it does not burn. And the scent does not last a long time.

Before Tilly realized what was happening, her father had grasped her by the skin of her neck. He darted through the opening of the den. He dragged Tilly on the ground. Inside, he dropped her.

Then, he backed out of the opening. The eagle was gone. And so was the fish!

Finally, it was time for Tilly and her brothers to learn to swim.

Otters do not know how to swim when they are born. They must be taught by their parents.

The mother otter went into the water and swam out a short distance. She looked at Tilly who was sitting on the sandy beach. She called Tilly with a loud chuckling sound.

Tilly knew she was being called. But she wondered why. Her mother was in the water. Surely she did not want Tilly to go in water. She had never been in water.

The mother called Tilly again.

The two male otters had followed their father a short distance up the riverbank. The father otter was showing them how to turn over rocks and find insects.

Tilly's mother came out of the water. She stretched out on the beach. Again, she called Tilly. Tilly thought her mother wanted to play. She climbed on her mother's back.

But the mother otter went back into the water. Tilly held tightly to her mother's fur. She was frightened. What was her mother trying to do to her?

Suddenly, the mother otter swam out from under Tilly. Tilly flipped over in the water.

Sometimes young otters cannot stay right side up in the water at first.

Tilly's mother swam back underneath her. Tilly turned over. She grasped the fur on her mother's back.

Again, the mother swam out from under Tilly. This time, she stayed right side up.

Her mother swam close to Tilly. Tilly began to paddle her feet. Faster. She was swimming just like her mother! What fun!

Within a few days, all three babies were swimming in the river with their parents.

When they were about two months old, the young otters were weaned. They began to catch fish by themselves. They missed more than they caught. But they were learning.

If they weren't eating or sleeping, they were playing. Otters play more than any other animals except maybe porpoises.

CHAPTER 5

It was time for the mother otter and her young to move. The father otter had left the family already. He was moving to a new area.

Otters do a lot of traveling. As soon as the food supply gets low, they move to another lake or river. Sometimes they move simply because they're wanderers.

Otters travel overland. This can be dangerous. When they are close to water, they can easily escape enemies. But on land they are easy targets.

It was early in the morning when Tilly's family left their cozy den in the riverbank. They started their long journey.

Tilly thought it was great fun. She and her siblings played as they went. They wrestled and bumped one another with their noses.

If they got too far behind, their mother would slow down and call them. If they got too far ahead, she would catch up with them. Then she would nip them on the noses.

Otters usually have regular routes that they travel. Some of the routes may be from 15 to 20 miles long. In winter, when food is scarce, they must travel farther than in the summer.

Males travel alone. Often they go much farther. Some even travel up to 100 miles.

Tilly's short legs grew tired. She slowed down. Her siblings slowed down. Mother made chirping sounds, calling them. But the young ones were too tired to move.

Otters are slow. They only move at high speeds when they are trying to escape danger. Even then, they cannot run fast for long periods of time.

For short distances, otters travel about 15 miles an hour. When they move fast, they leap, hunching their backs. They look like huge inchworms.

Finally, the mother otter moved to some bushes growing nearby. She began to eat something off the bushes.

Tilly got up. She moved to where her mother was. She watched her mother take a small, round, blue thing from the bush and eat it.

Tilly tried one. It was sour. She shook her head and twitched her nose. Then she tried another one. It was a little riper. She liked it.

The brothers joined Tilly and their mother. They all filled up on huckleberries. It was a new treat for the young otters. Tilly thought huckleberries were good. But she liked fish better.

After the berry feast, Tilly and her
siblings rested. The mother rested too.

Then once more, the otters were on their
way. They came to a big, open meadow

where four deer were lying in the grass.
Tilly stopped and stood on her hind legs.
She stretched herself tall. Her eyes grew
large. What were these huge creatures?

The mother was standing on her hind legs too. She was watching the strange creatures. Tilly moved closer to her mother.

The mother otter was not frightened. She was only curious. She had seen deer many times. She knew they were no threat.

The family moved on. They stopped once at a small marsh. They rolled and rolled in the wet grass. They caught and ate some salamanders. The mother otter caught a frog.

When they finished eating, they played. The young otters chased one another around and around. They tumbled on the ground, chirping like birds. Their mother played too.

After a long time, they flopped down and began to groom one another. They fluffed one another's hair. Then they slept.

At last, they reached a large lake. It was
new to Tilly and her brothers. But the
mother otter had been there many times.
This would be their home for several

weeks. Then they would move on to
another place.

Later, they would return to the place
where Tilly and her brothers had been born.

CHAPTER 6

It was winter. Ice covered part of the river. There was snow on the ground. Some days, the temperatures were below freezing.

But the cold weather didn't bother Tilly. She had a thick, warm coat. She had a den under a tangle of tree roots.

She was on her own now. Her brothers had gone their own ways too. It had only been a short time since Tilly had left her mother. Her mother would be having a new litter in the early spring. Tilly would not have her first litter for another year.

But Tilly never got bored or lonely. She loved to play, even when she was all alone. She especially liked the snow.

Sliding down snow-covered hills was lots of fun for Tilly. Sometimes other lone otters joined her.

Tilly had become a very skilled hunter. Ice did not stop her from catching fish. She would find a hole in the ice. She would swim around under the ice and breathe the bubbles of air trapped against the ice.

Otters can let out their breath underwater. Then they breathe back the bubbles that form under the ice. When the river or lake is frozen over, it is easy to catch fish. The fish cannot swim very fast in cold water.

All over the forest and meadows, animals were hibernating or holed up. Animals that holed up stored food to eat.

Otters do not hibernate. And they do not hole up. The cold does not bother them. And they do not need to store food.

Tilly had fun playing with other otters in the area. All the otters got along very well together. They hardly ever fought among themselves.

When otters do fight, they can be quite mean. They will fight to defend themselves and their young. It would be dangerous to get between a mother otter and her babies.

Emil Lier was a man who studied otters.

In 1928, he got a pair of otters. Over the years, he raised hundreds of them. He trained some of his otters for hunting game birds. Lier claimed otters could find as many birds as hunting dogs.

Lier found that otters made wonderful pets. He described them as playful, gentle, and social animals.

Once when Emil Lier was walking with his otters and his dog, another dog attacked. At once, his otters attacked the attacker and sent it howling across the field.

Another time, Lier himself was attacked by a strange dog. His otters came to his defense.

People have made pets of river otters. They are affectionate and playful. And they are very clean. But it is never a good idea to make pets of wild animals.

When spring came, Tilly traveled to a new area. It was at a large lake. The hunting was good. There were lots of fish in the lake and in the creek nearby. There

were a few other otters in the area.

It would be a good place to live. At least for now, it was a good place.

Later a lot of people would come to fish on the lake. Motorboats on the water would make the otters nervous. They would no longer feel safe.

Along the edge of the lake were thousands of minnows. They made very tasty meals. Water insects lived there too.

Tilly found good places to roll about in the mud and grass. That was how she kept her fur clean.

People who came to the lake to camp and fish enjoyed watching the otters. But the otters were nervous when people got too close. More than once, Tilly had her picture taken.

In the middle of the night, when the campers were sleeping, the otters played in the water. Their play lasted for hours.

The following spring, Tilly had her first litter. She had made her nest in an old muskrat house. It was cozy and snug. Tilly had three babies. They were all males.

For the next few months, she cared for them. She cleaned them, nursed them, and kept them warm.

When they were ready, she taught them to swim. She taught them just as her mother had taught her.

Often she played with her babies. She frisked about with them in the tall grass. She played games with them in the water.

It didn't matter that she was an adult and a mother. That was the best part of being an otter. An otter never has to really grow up.

FOR MORE INFORMATION, CONTACT

International Otter Survival Fund
Skye Environmental Centre Ltd
Broadford
Isle of Skye IV49 9AQ
International Tel/Fax: ++44(1471) 822 487
email: iosf@otter.org
Web site: www.otter.org

The River Otter Alliance
6733 S. Locust Court
Englewood, CO 80112
email: skipper@otternet.com
Web site: otternet.com